Mathematics Kindergarten

TABLE OF CONTENTS

Page Number(s)

NUMBERS & EARLY MATH

Mathematics Kindergarten
Numbers & Early Math

Materials You Will Need:

❑ A good pencil (or 2) with a working eraser

❑ Crayons

Check your work with the Answer Key at the back of this book!

Benefits of Numbers & Early Math:

❑ Learn about geometric shapes & patterns.

❑ Practice sorting and classifying objects.

❑ Count, write, and recognize numbers 0-20!

❑ Strengthen your skills with addition and subtraction.

❑ Enjoy practicing and learning about math!

Parent & Teacher Coaching Tips:

❑ *Prepare.* Provide your child with a quiet, well-lit place to work on important skills. Prepare a desk or table with an upright chair that is comfortable. Make sure that your child has plenty of room to work and spread out materials. Allow your child enough space to move around as well.

❑ *Plan.* Choose a practice time that seems to work well for your child. Include your child in this scheduling process and select a time when your child is well-rested and alert. Be sure to allow a break from working after a long school day. Young children will need short practice sessions and frequent breaks.

❑ *Enjoy.* Use your child's learning strengths to reinforce information AND build new skills with your child. Encourage FUN through movement, play, acting, writing, drawing, singing, music, talking, thinking, and more while you work with your child. Be silly and allow your child to laugh, tell jokes, and move around as you work. **Having fun will extend your child's ability to stay on task!**

❑ *Break.* Take frequent breaks from working. Throughout the book, you will find built-in review pages after each section of skills. When your child completes the section, use the book mark to mark your place in the book. Mark the skill checklist and take a break.

❑ *Relax!* Your role is critical in helping your child succeed with this workbook, at school, and with standardized tests. Be sure to help your child: eat well, sleep well, practice deep-breathing techniques to relax, visualize success, and release energy in a physical way (running, walking, playing sports). Young children need to learn and practice these skills, too!

❑ *Talk.* Encourage your child to talk about feelings related to testing, help your child understand the need for tests AND stress the value of <u>real</u> learning that is not always obvious with test scores.

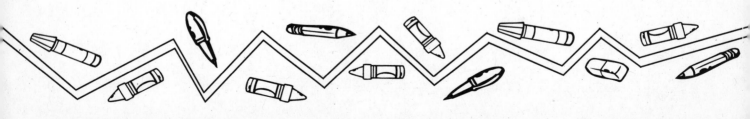

Name:_____ Date:_____

  In each row, color the ones that are the **same**.
Draw an X on the one that is **different** from the rest.

Name:_____ Date:_____

 Draw an X on the object that does <u>not</u> belong in each group.

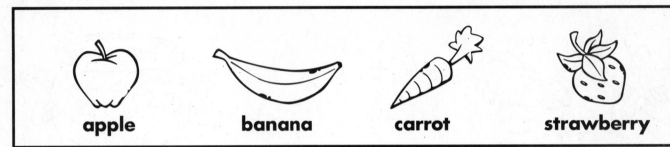

| apple | banana | carrot | strawberry |

| paintbrush | flower | pencil | crayon |

| airplane | elephant | monkey | giraffe |

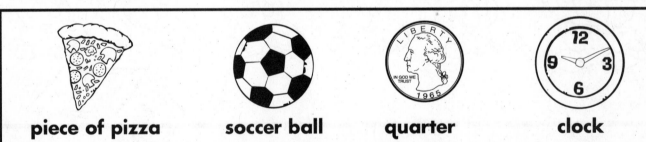

| piece of pizza | soccer ball | quarter | clock |

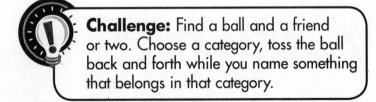

Challenge: Find a ball and a friend or two. Choose a category, toss the ball back and forth while you name something that belongs in that category.

Tip: Think about what the pictures have in common. Look at the shape of the objects, too.

Sorting & classifying

Draw a line to match the animal and the home that belong together.

Name:_____ Date:_____

Review: Sorting & Classifying

 In each group, color the one that does <u>not</u> belong.

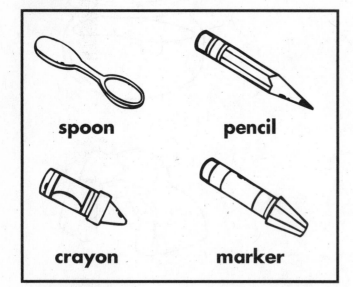

spoon **pencil**

crayon **marker**

drum **carrot**

kite **teddy bear**

  Draw and color another object that belongs in each group.

strawberry **banana**

watermelon

cake **cupcakes**

cookies

STOP! TAKE A BREAK! You did a great job! Place your Book Mark here & RELAX!

Count how many in each group. Draw a line to match each group of fish to the correct number.

   **1**

   **2**

   **3**

   **4**

   **5**

 Challenge: Swim like a fish around your table 5 times. Then, color the fish in each group with a different color!

Counting to 5; matching numerals with the correct number of objects   7

Name:_____   Date:_____

  Count how many in each group. Draw a line to match the groups with the **same** number of objects.

8   Understanding numbers; matching sets of 1-5

Count how many in each group.
Circle the correct number.

 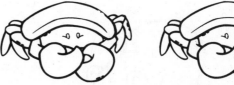

2 **4** **1**   **3** **2** **5**

1 **3** **5**   **3** **2** **1**

Use the number code to color the dinosaurs.

1 = (((yellow)) 2 = ((orange))

3 = ((brown)) 4 = ((blue)) 5 = ((green))

 Challenge: Count all the dinosaurs. Then, count the tails, count the feet, count the teeth, and count the eyes! What else can you count?

1   2   3   4   5
one   **two**   **three**   **four**   **five**

  Count the sweets in each group.
Write each number word.

   **1**

   **2**

   **3**

   **4**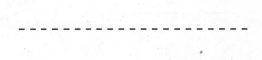

   **5**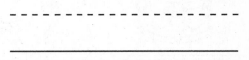

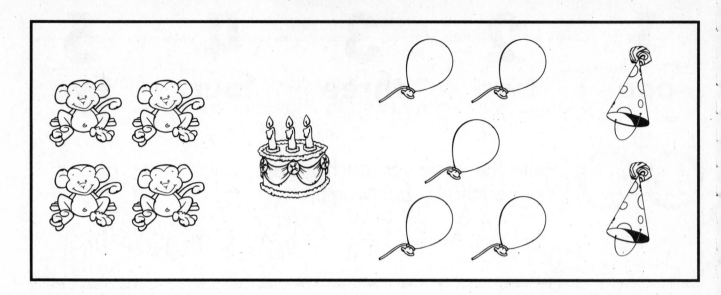

 Count the objects in the picture above. Then, write the correct number below each picture to show how many.

- - - - - - - -

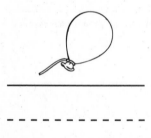

- - - - - - - -

- - - - - - - -

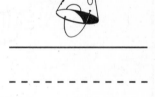

Tip:
Color, or draw
an X on each item
as you count.

Name:_____   Date:_____

Review: Numbers 1 to 5

  Trace each number. Then, color the correct number of animals in each group to show the number.

one 1	    
two 2	  
three 3	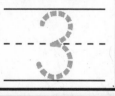     
four 4	     
five 5	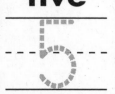   

Name:_____ Date:_____

Review: Numbers 1 to 5

  Draw and color more food pieces for each animal to make 5 in each group.

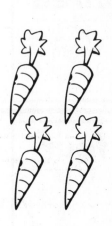

STOP! TAKE A BREAK! You did a great job! Place your Book Mark here & RELAX!

Color the shapes that are the **same** in each row.

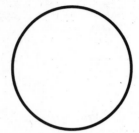  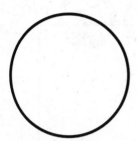

  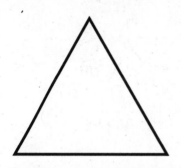

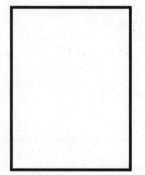 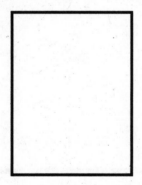 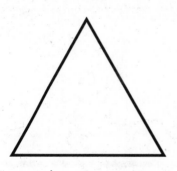

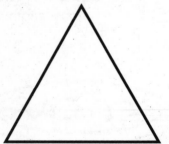 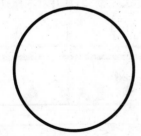 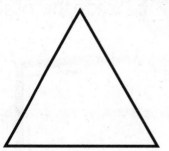

 Challenge: Can you name each shape that you see on this page? Count the sides on each shape, too!

Identifying shapes

Name:_____ Date:_____

   Trace the **squares**. Then, draw your own **squares** and count them.

 Color the objects that are shaped like a ☐.

Tip:
All 4 sides of a **square** are the same length.

16   Recognizing and drawing squares

Name:_____   Date:_____

   Trace the **circles**. Then, draw your own **circles** and count them.

  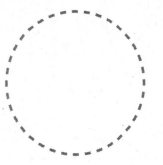 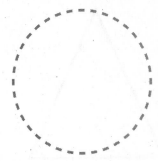

 Color the objects that are shaped like a ◯.

Name:_____ Date:_____

   Trace the **triangles**. Then, draw your own **triangles** and count them.

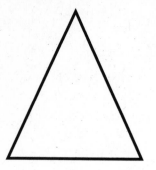 

Tip:
A **triangle** always has 3 straight sides. The sides can be different lengths!

 Color the objects that are shaped like a △.

Recognizing and drawing triangles

Trace the **rectangles**. Then, draw your own **rectangles** and count them.

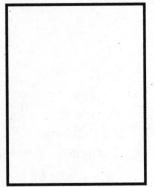 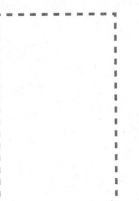 

Tip:
A **rectangle** is like a square, but 2 sides are long and 2 sides are short.

 Color the objects that are shaped like a ☐.

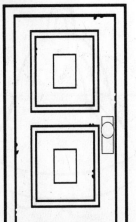

 Challenge: Point to the 2 long sides on each **rectangle** you see on this page.

Recognizing and drawing rectangles

Trace the **ovals**. Then, draw your own **ovals** and count them.

 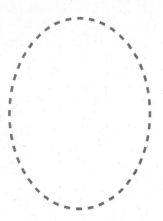 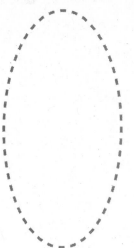

Tip: An **oval** is like a skinny circle.

 Color the objects that are shaped like an ◯.

  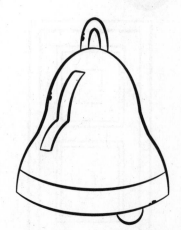

Trace the **diamonds**. Then, draw your own **diamonds** and count them.

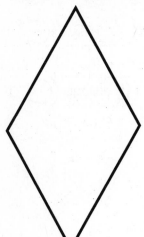 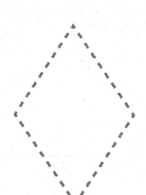 

Tip:
A **diamond** is like a stretched out square!

 Color all these kites that are shaped like ◇.

Recognizing and drawing diamonds

Name:_____ Date:_____

  Draw the shape that comes next in each **pattern**. Use the code to color the shapes.

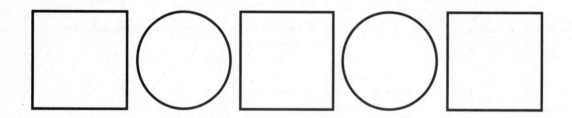

☐ = yellow   ○ = purple   ◇ = blue

△ = red   ⬭ = green   ▭ = orange

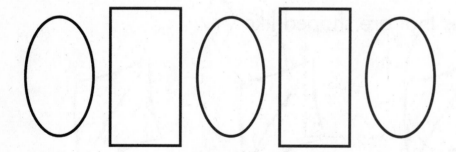

 Challenge: Find something in your home that has each shape you learned about: a **square**, a **circle**, a **triangle**, a **rectangle**, and an **oval**.

Name:_____   Date:_____

  Draw the shape that comes next in each **pattern**.
Color the shapes to match the words inside them.

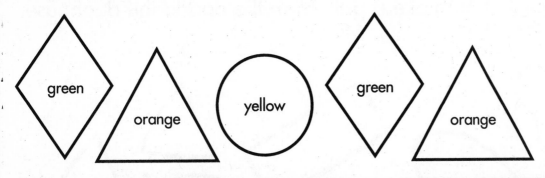

green   orange   yellow   green   orange

purple   red   purple   red

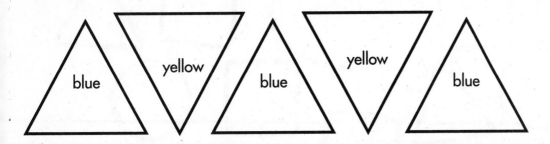

blue   yellow   blue   yellow   blue

purple   red   red   purple   red

Tip:
Sound out the
color words in
each shape.

 Challenge: On another piece of paper,
draw your own shape **patterns**. See if a
family member can add shapes to continue
your **pattern**.

Name:_____ Date:_____

Review: Shapes

 Color the ☐ s to make a path from the dog to the doghouse.

 Challenge: Which shape can you make by arranging 4 crayons? Which shape can you make with 3 crayons? Which shapes cannot be formed by using crayons with straight edges?

Name:_____   Date:_____

Review: Shapes

  Trace all the shapes. Then, use the shape code to color the picture.

⬭ = red   ◯ = blue   △ = green

▭ = yellow   ▢ = orange   ◇ = purple

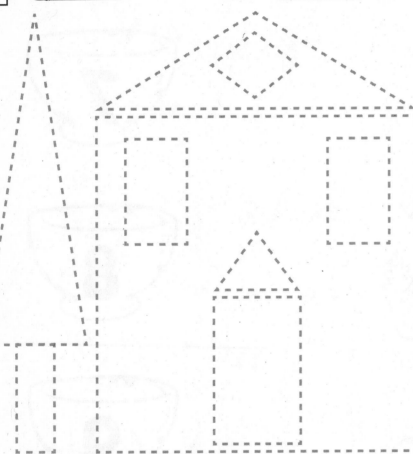 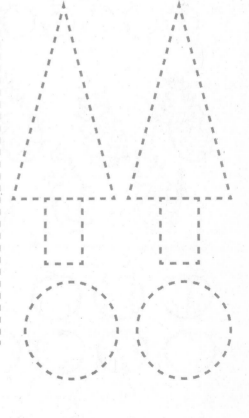

STOP! **TAKE A BREAK!** **You did a great job!** Place your Book Mark here & RELAX!

Name:_____   Date:_____

  Count the objects in each group. Then, draw a line to match each group to the number that shows how many.

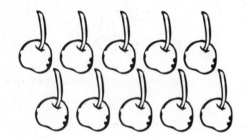

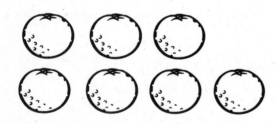

Counting to 10; matching numerals with the correct number of objects

Name:_____   Date:_____

  Count how many in each group. Circle the correct number.

6   **7**   8

7   8   9

8   9   10

6   8   9

7   8   10

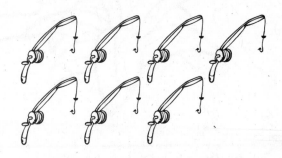

6   7   9

Draw a line to connect the dots from **1** to **10**. Color the picture.

 Challenge: On another sheet of paper, design your own dot-to-dot picture. Use the numbers **1** to **10**. Have a family member complete your dot-to-dot.

Tip: Count out loud as you connect the dots.

Name:_____ Date:_____

Tip:
Look at the numbers
on the hanging
opossum family
for help.

 Write the number that comes between the given numbers.

1 2 3   7 9

6 8   4 6

3 5   8 10

6 six   **7** seven   **8** eight   **9** nine   **10** ten

  Count the treats in each group. Write the number word.

   **6**   _six_

   **7**   _____

   **8**   _____

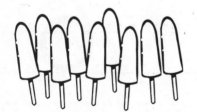   **9**   _____

   **10**   _____

Name:_____   Date:_____

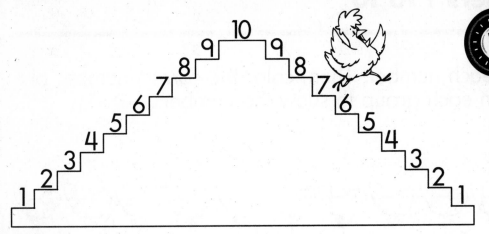

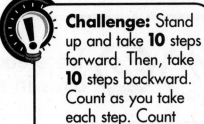

Challenge: Stand up and take **10** steps forward. Then, take **10** steps backward. Count as you take each step. Count the steps in your home, too!

 Write the numbers forward from **1** to **10**.

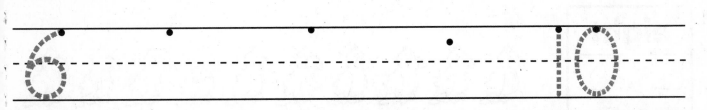

 Write the numbers backward from **10** to **1**.

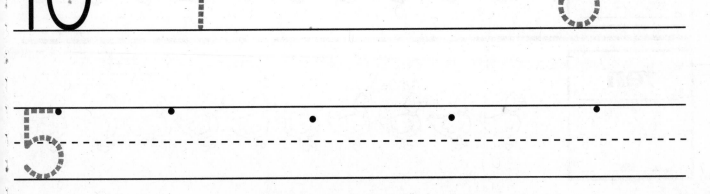

Name:_____   Date:_____

Review: Numbers 1 to 10

 Trace each number. Then, color the correct number of birds in each group to show the number.

six 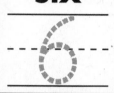	
seven 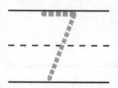	
eight 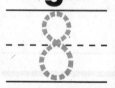	
nine 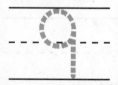	
ten 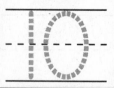	

Name:_____   Date:_____

Review: Numbers 1 to 10

  Count the objects in each group. Circle the number that shows how many.

1   **2**   **3**

6   **7**   **8**

8   **9**   **10**

4   **5**   **6**

2   **3**   **4**

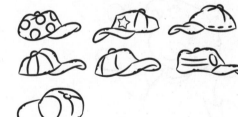

7   **8**   **9**

 STOP! **TAKE A BREAK!** You did a great job! Place your Book Mark here & RELAX!

Color the picture in each group that shows **more** objects.

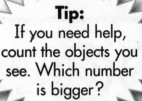
Tip:
If you need help, count the objects you see. Which number is bigger?

Measurement: Comparing quantity

Name:_____ Date:_____

 Color the picture in each group that shows **fewer** objects.

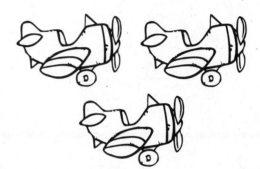

In each row, color the animals that are the **same** size.

 Challenge: Find something in your home that is about the **same** size as you.

Name:_____   Date:_____

  Color the **bigger** animal. Circle the **smaller** animal.

Tip:
Small and **little** mean the same thing!

 Challenge: Draw a **big** snack for each **bigger** animal. Draw a **small** snack for each **smaller** animal.

In each group, color the **longer** animal yellow and color the **shorter** animal green.

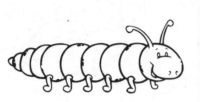

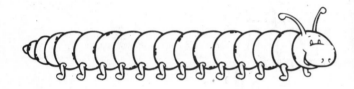

 Challenge: Find 3 items in your home that are **longer** than a pencil. Find 3 items that are **shorter** than a pencil.

In each group, color the **taller** object red and color the **shorter** object blue.

 Challenge: Look at the red and blue crayon you are using for this page. Hold them up next to each other. Which crayon is **taller**, and which one is **shorter**?

In each group, color the object that is **heavier** and circle the object that is **lighter**.

Measurement: Comparing weight

Name:_____   Date:_____

Review: Comparing Quantity & Size

 Count the balloons. Then, draw your own picture to show **more** balloons.

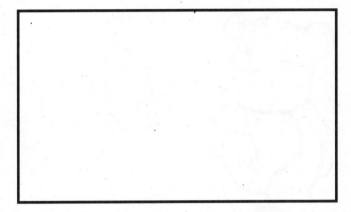

 Count the birds. Then, draw your own picture to show **fewer** birds.

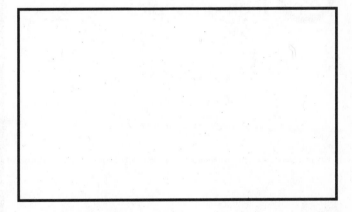

 Draw something that is **longer** than the dotted line below.

- -

Name:_____ Date:_____

Review: Comparing Quantity & Size

  Color the animals that are **bigger** than the monkey.
Circle the animals that are **smaller** than the monkey.

 Draw something **heavier** than an apple.

Draw something **lighter** than a backpack.

TAKE A BREAK! You did a great job!
Place your Book Mark here & RELAX!

11 12 13 14 15 16 17 18 19 20

  Count the objects in each group. Write the number to show how many.

12	_____
_____	_____
_____	_____
_____	_____

Name:_____ Date:_____

  Count the objects in each group. Draw a line to match the group to the correct number.

18

20

11

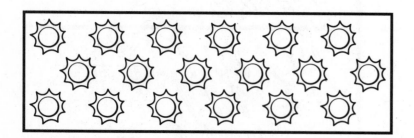

14

12

Name:_____ Date:_____

 Count the fish and write how many.
Then, color all the fish.

_____

- - - - - - - - - - - -

_____

 Trace all the numbers. Then, write the numbers that are missing on each line.

Tip:
Look at the numbers on the opossum family if you need help.

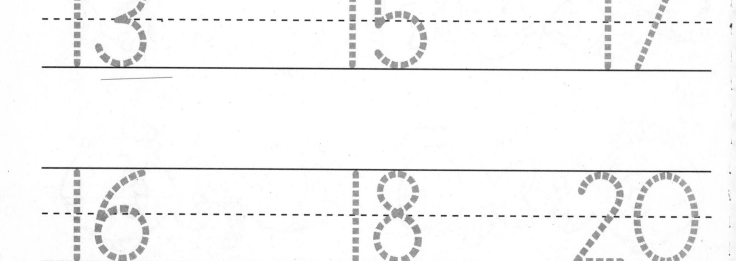

Name:_____   Date:_____

Review: Numbers 1 to 20

 Draw 5 △s, 5 ⬭s, 5 ▢s, and 20 ◯s on the pizza. Then, color the toppings according to the code.

△ yellow   ⬭ green   ▢ brown   ◯ red

Tip: Count each shape topping as you draw it!

Challenge: Count how many toppings in all.

Name:_____ Date:_____

Review: Numbers 1 to 20

  Draw a line to connect the dots from **1** to **20**. Color the picture.

In each row, count the objects in the first group and the second group. Then, count them all together. Write the number to show how many in all.

    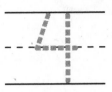 4

    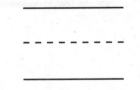

Name:_____ Date:_____

  In each row, count the objects in the first group and the second group. Then, count them all together.

Write the number to show how many in all.

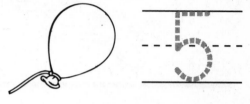
Tip:
Counting all of the items together is the same as adding!

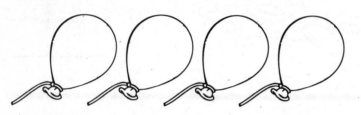 

 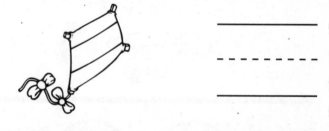

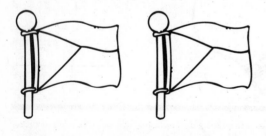 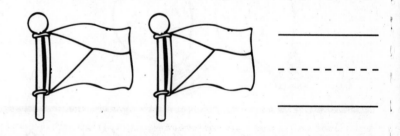

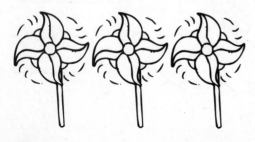 

Addition

4   **+**   **2**   **=**   **6**

  Count and write how many in the first group, then the second group. Next, count them all together. Write the number to show how many in all.

_5_   **+**   _5_   **=**   _____

_____   **+**   _____   **=**   _____

_____   **+**   _____   **=**   _____

_____   **+**   _____   **=**   _____

Count the objects in the first group and the second group. Then, count them all together. Write the number to show how many all.

$$\begin{array}{r} 2 \\ +\,1 \\ \hline 3 \end{array}$$

  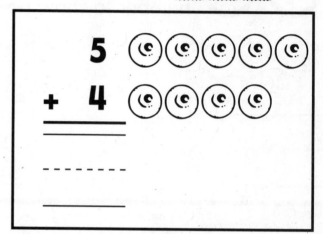

$$\begin{array}{r} 4 \\ +\,3 \\ \hline \end{array}$$
- - - - - -

$$\begin{array}{r} 5 \\ +\,4 \\ \hline \end{array}$$
- - - - - -

$$\begin{array}{r} 3 \\ +\,3 \\ \hline \end{array}$$
- - - - - -

$$\begin{array}{r} 2 \\ +\,3 \\ \hline \end{array}$$
- - - - - -

$$\begin{array}{r} 1 \\ +\,2 \\ \hline \end{array}$$
- - - - - -

$$\begin{array}{r} 4 \\ +\,0 \\ \hline \end{array}$$
- - - - - -

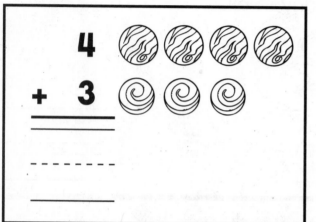

Name:_____   Date:_____

Review: Addition

  Count the items in each group. Then, add or count them all together. Write the number to show how many.

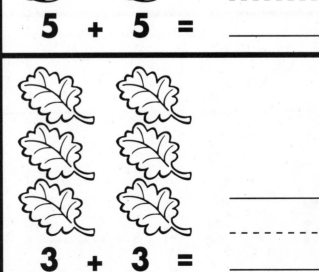

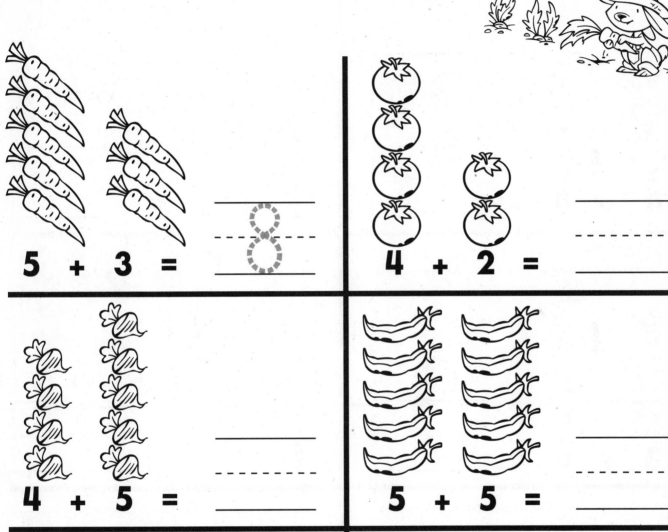

5 + 3 = 8

4 + 2 = _____

4 + 5 = _____

5 + 5 = _____

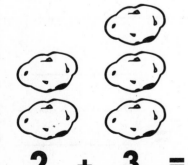

2 + 3 = _____

3 + 3 = _____

Name:_____   Date:_____

Review: Addition

 Count the items in each group. Then, add or count them all together. Write the number to show how many.

4 + 4 =

5 + 2 = _____

3 + 4 = _____

1 + 5 = _____

1 + 3 = _____

2 + 2 = _____

Name:_____   Date:_____

  Count all the objects. Subtract, or take away, 1 object in each group. Count how many are left and write the number.

Tip:
Cross out 1 object in each group to show how many you are subtracting.

   4 - 1 =   3

   3 - 1 = _____

5 - 1 = _____

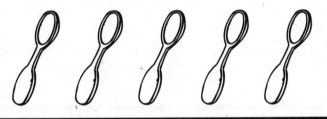   6 - 1 = _____

   2 - 1 = _____

Count all the objects. Subtract, or take away, 2 objects in each group. Count how many are left and write the number.

Tip:
Cross out 2 objects in each group to show how many you are subtracting.

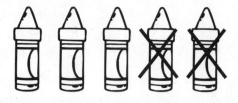

5 − 2 = _3_

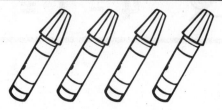

4 − 2 = _____

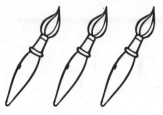

3 − 2 = _____

2 − 2 = _____

6 − 2 = _____

Count the keys in each row. Subtract, or take away, the number of keys shown at the beginning of each row. Count how many are left and write the number.

Tip:
Don't forget to cross out the number of objects you are subtracting!

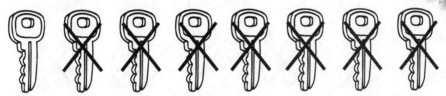

Subtract 7.   **8 − 7 = _____**

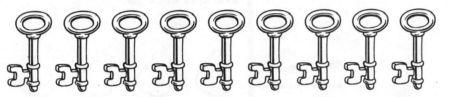

Subtract 5.   **9 − 5 = _____**

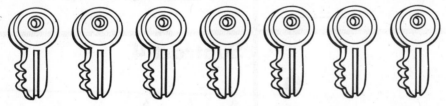

Subtract 4.   **7 − 4 = _____**

Subtract 3.   **6 − 3 = _____**

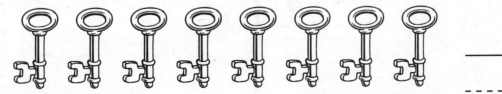

Subtract 2.   **8 − 2 = _____**

Name:_____ Date:_____

  Count the fruit pieces in each group. Subtract the number shown. Count how many are left and write the number.

Tip:
Don't forget to cross out the number of objects you are subtracting!

$$10 - 5$$

5

Subtract 3.

$$9 - 3$$

_ _ _ _ _

Subtract 2.

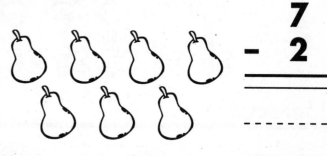

$$7 - 2$$

_ _ _ _ _

Subtract 5.

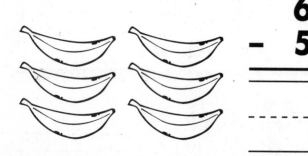

$$6 - 5$$

_ _ _ _ _

Subtract 4.

$$10 - 4$$

_ _ _ _ _

Subtract 8.

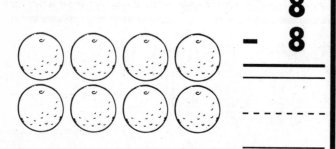

$$8 - 8$$

_ _ _ _ _

Subtract 1.

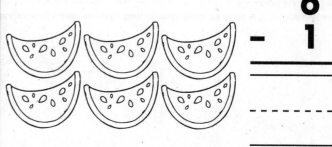

$$6 - 1$$

_ _ _ _ _

Name:_____   Date:_____

Review: Subtraction

  Count the instruments in each group. Subtract the number shown. Count how many are left and write the number.

Tip: Cross out the number of objects you are subtracting!

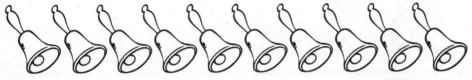

Subtract 6.   **10 – 6 =** _4_

Subtract 7.   **9 – 7 =** _____

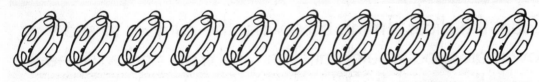

Subtract 5.   **8 – 5 =** _____

Subtract 8.   **10 – 8 =** _____

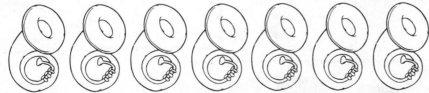

Subtract 3.   **7 – 3 =** _____

Name:_____ Date:_____

Review: Subtraction

  Count the snacks in each group. Subtract how many snacks each friend will eat. Write how many are left.

Subtract 5.  **6 – 5 =** _____

Subtract 3. **7 – 3 =** _____

Subtract 2. **5 – 2 =** _____

Subtract 7. **9 – 7 =** _____

 Count the slices. In the box, write the number to show how many you would eat. Then, subtract and write how many slices are left.

5 – [____] **=** _____

 STOP! **TAKE A BREAK!** You did a great job!
Place your Book Mark here & RELAX!

Review: Subtraction

Answer Key

Please take time to review the work your child or student has completed. Remember to praise both success and effort. If your child makes a mistake, let him or her know that mistakes are a part of learning. Explain why the incorrect response was not the best choice. Then, encourage your child to think it through and select a better choice.

page 3
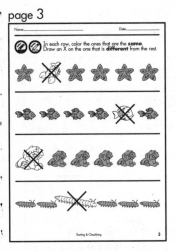

page 4

page 5
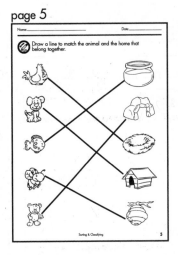

page 6

page 7
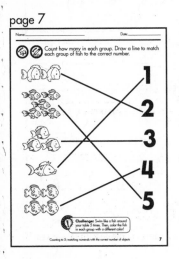

page 8

page 9
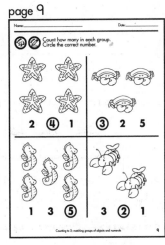

page 10
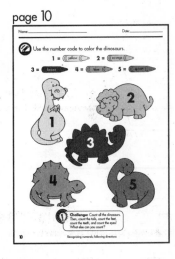

page 11
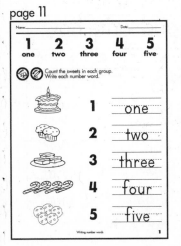

page 12

page 13
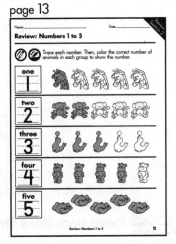

page 14

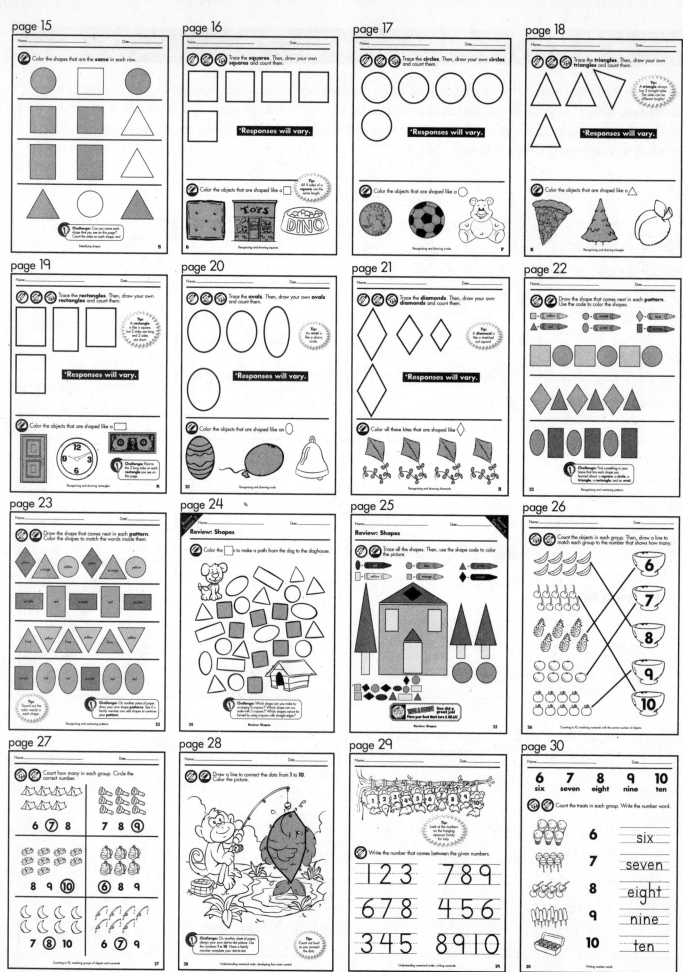

Answers

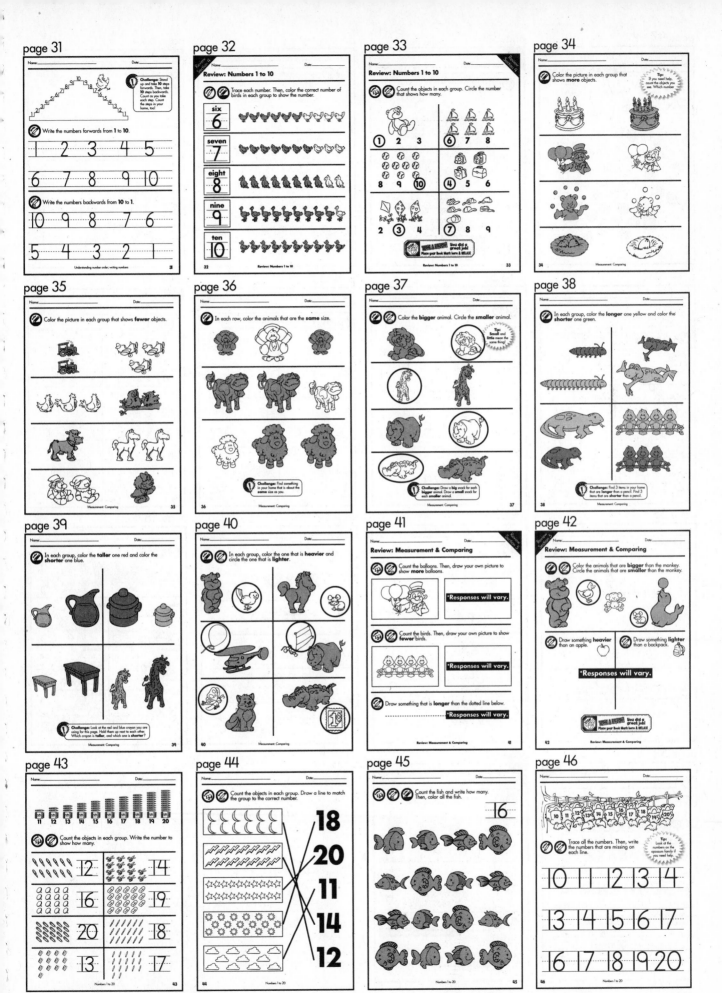

Answers

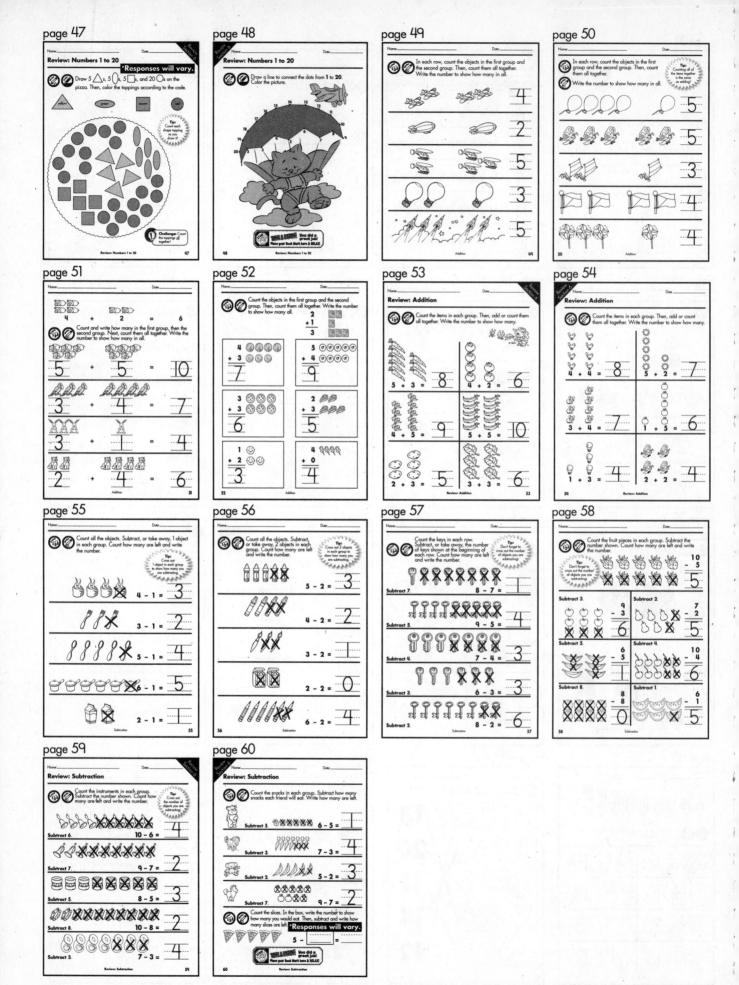

Answers

NUMBERS & SHAPES!

1. Tear out the game boards & find a chip, paper scrap, or penny for a marker.
2. Have a friend or family member say a number or shape out loud.
3. Find that number word or shape and cover it with your marker.

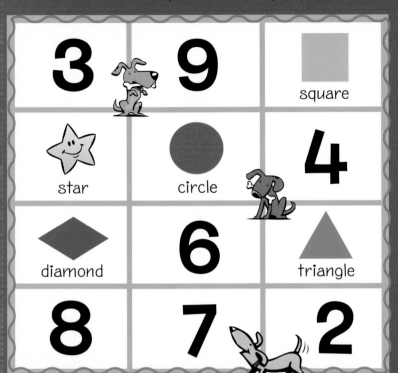

3	9	square
star	circle	4
diamond	6	triangle
8	7	2

CUT HERE

SQUARE SORTS! #1

1. Tear out the game board and cut out the squares along the lines.
2. Sort the squares into different groups and describe your reason for the different groups. Sort again in a different way.
3. Create a category pattern using the squares (i.e. fruit, vehicle, fruit, vehicle). What are some other ways to use the square cards? Make up your own sorting games!

train	car	truck	cookies
lollipop	cupcake	heart	ice cream
plane	square	donut	star
popsicle	helicopter	triangle	motorcycle

_____'s
Your Name

BOOK MARK!
Use this Book Mark to save your spot in the book.

GREAT JOB!

That was DOG-GONE fabulous!

TAKE A BREAK!

_____'s

Your Name

SKILL CHECKLIST

SUPER COOL!

Use this Skill Checklist to check off the skills as you practice them in the book.

- ☐ Sorting & Classifying
- ☐ Counting to 20
- ☐ Writing Numbers
- ☐ Adding & Subtracting
- ☐ More & Fewer
- ☐ Tall, Short & Long
- ☐ Big & Little
- ☐ Heavy & Light

ADDITION BINGO!

1. Tear out the game boards & use some chips, paper scraps, or pennies for your bingo markers.
2. Have a friend of family member say an addition sum from 1-10.
3. Find a matching equation. (i.e. Sum of 10 - cover 10+0)
4. Continue covering equations until you have 3 in a row!

2+2	3+5	4+5
7+2	3+4	6+4
1+1	9+0	2+3

CUT HERE

SQUARE SORTS! #2

1. Tear out the game board and cut out the squares along the.
2. Sort the squares into different groups and describe your reason for the different groups. Sort again in a different way.
3. Create a category pattern using the squares (i.e. fruit, vehicle, fruit, vehicle). What are some other ways to use the square cards?

bird	orange	banana	oval
frog	snail	blueberry	fish
circle	apple	rabbit	diamond
rectangle	strawberry	sheep	pear